FEVER

wise publications
london / new york / paris / sydney / copenhagen / berlin / madrid / tokyo

exclusive distributors:
music sales limited
8/9 frith street, london w1b 3jb, england.
music sales pty limited
120 rothschild avenue, rosebery, nsw 2018,
australia.

order no. AM973643
isbn 0-7119-9278-9
this book © copyright 2001 by wise publications.

music arrangements by jack long.
music processed by paul ewers music design.
cover image courtesy of parlophone records.
additional images: london features international.

printed in the united kingdom by
printwise (haverhill) limited, haverhill, suffolk.

your guarantee of quality:
as publishers, we strive to produce every
book to the highest commercial standards.
while endeavouring to retain the original running
order of the recorded album, the book has been
carefully designed to minimise awkward page
turns and to make playing from it a real pleasure.
particular care has been given to specifying
acid-free, neutral-sized paper made from
pulps which have not been elemental chlorine
bleached. this pulp is from farmed sustainable
forests and was produced with special regard
for the environment. throughout, the printing
and binding have been planned to ensure a
sturdy, attractive publication which should give
years of enjoyment. if your copy fails to meet
our high standards, please inform us and we
will gladly replace it.

www.musicsales.com

more more more

words & music by tommy d & liz winstanley

1. Here am I with my de - sire:— feel it burn-ing just for— you.—
(Verse 2 see block lyric)

My oh my, this love di - vine—— is

tak - ing me to some - where new.—— Just

slide,——————————— get your bo - dy down, down,— down;—

09

Verse 2:
Here am I, and deep inside
I've got a little spot for you.
Ooh, make me sigh with sheer delight
As, baby, you caress and soothe.
So slide
I wanna feel you down, down, down
And glide
You know I need you all around.

love at first sight

words & music by kylie minogue, richard stannard,
julian gallagher, ash howes & martin harrington

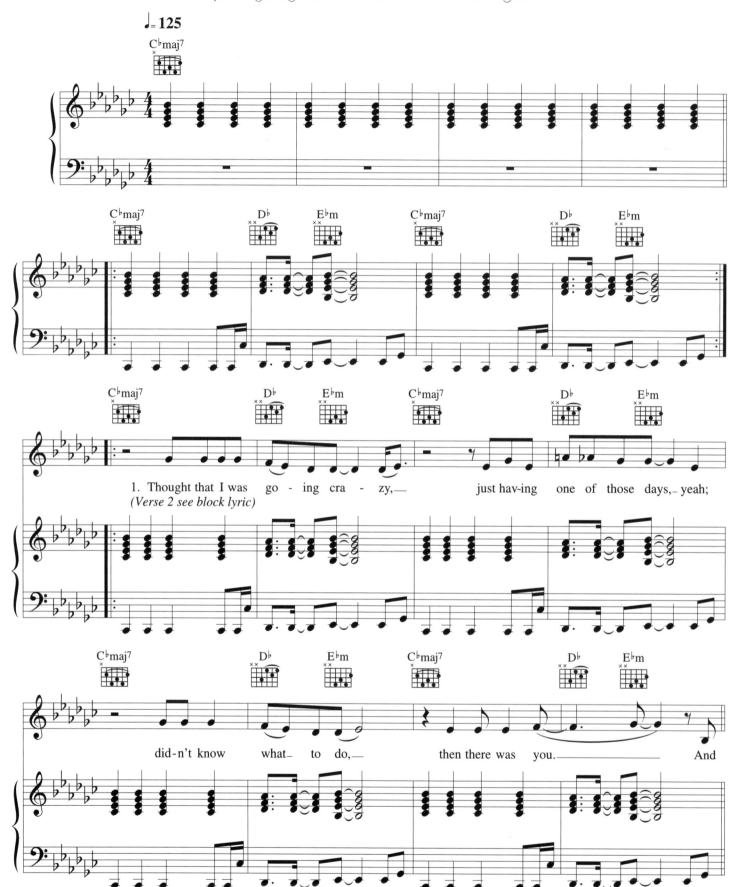

time,   I   knew   we   were   meant   to   be   as

one.

one.

ba - by —— when —— I —— heard— you for the—— first——

—— time,—— I knew we were—— meant—— to—— be—— as

1.

one.————

2.

one.———————————— It was love,——

Verse 2:
Was tired of running out of luck
Thinking 'bout giving up, yeah
Didn't know what to do
Then there was you.

And everything went from wrong to right *etc.*

can't get you out of my head

words & music by cathy dennis & rob davis

(La la la la la la la la la la la la la la la la.)

(La la la la la la la la la la la la la la la la.
I just

Stay_____ for -
ev - er____ and ev - er____ and ev - er____ and ev - er._____
(La la la la___ la la la la la la la la___ la la la la.

Repeat ad lib. to fade

Verse 2:
There's a dark secret in me
Don't leave me locked in your heart
Set me free *etc.*

fever

words & music by greg fitzgerald & tom nichols

1. I've been bit-ten by the bug, and I'm com-ing down with oh, some-thing that can't be cured.—
(Verse 2 see block lyric)

— There ain't a doc-tor in this town who is more qua-li-fied than

can't___ help but need this drug. Don't you feel the

fe - ver like___ I do?_____ *(Spoken):* Feel the fever!

Verse 2:

I'm ready for the news, so tell me straight

Hey, doctor, just what do you diagnose?

There ain't a surgeon like you any place in all the world

So, now shall I remove my clothes?

So tell me, what do you advise for these symptoms?

Heart beating faster, and work is a disaster, ah!

I'm lovesick when you're not around

Check me over.

When strong hands are healing

I'm dancing on the ceiling.

give it to me

words & music by kylie minogue, mark picchiotti & steve anderson

Verse 2:

I need a shot of love
'Cause I got a bad, bad habit
Can't seem to get enough
Give it to me 'cause I gotta have it!
Here we go, let's go down
Move to the rhythm that is in my mind.
Here we go, let's go now
I'm the lead, follow me
For a real good time.

Give it, give it to *etc.*

come into my world

words & music by cathy dennis & rob davis

Verse 2:
Take these lips that were made for kissing
And this heart that will see you through
And these hands that were made to touch and feel you.

So free your love.
Hear me, I'm calling.

fragile
words & music by rob davis

And I'm fra - gile when___ I___ hear___ ___ you speak;___ fra - gile, feel - ing___ small.___

This could be___ the clos - est thing___ to___ love.___

But

Verse 2:
Shake and sweat, wipe my brow
Scared of what's to come.
Lie awake, toss and turn
Am I the only one?

But I get butterflies *etc.*

in your eyes

words & music by kylie minogue, richard stannard, julian gallagher & ash howes

1. What on earth am I meant to do? In this crowd-ed place there— is
(Verse 2 see block lyric)

on - ly— you. Was gon-na leave,— now I have to stay.

It's no sur - prise, I've been watch - ing you late - ly;

1.
I want to make it with you.

2.
you. (With you, with you, with you, with you, with you, with

you, with you, with you, with you, with you, with you, with

Verse 2:
Destiny has a funny way
When it comes and takes all your cares away
I can't think of a single thing
Other than what a beautiful state I'm in.

dancefloor

words & music by steve anderson & cathy dennis

Verse 2:

Had your chance, but baby you blew it
You never loved me, and baby you knew it
And every time that you messed with my mind
I still believed in you.
('Cause I've had enough)
I'm sick and tired of pleasing you.
(Have I had your love?)
Is that the best that you can do?
You can keep on changing your mind
But you're way out of line.
'Cause if you think you've got me
If you think you've got me
Boy, just watch me.

(On the dancefloor) *etc.*

your love

words & music by kylie minogue, pascal gabriel & paul statham

1. Op - en your eyes to the skies up a - bove.
(Verse 2 see block lyric)

Verse 2:
Open your eyes to the skies and the sun
I wonder if this day will be the one.
Want you to hear my confession
You're my obsession
Do what you will do, but I can't help the way I'm wanting you.

burning up

words & music by greg fitzgerald & tom nichols

Verse 2:
My pulse is pumping
My heart may burst
If you drink me up
I'm gonna quench your thirst
Mm, mm, mm.
You're not that honest
No, you're not that nice
But if I kiss you once
I'm gonna kiss you twice
Mm, mm, mm.

love affair

words & music by kylie minogue, richard stannard & julian gallagher

1. Here in the mo - ment I___ be - long___
(Verse 2 see block lyric)

Verse 2:
Now we've only just begun
We're running out of time
I don't wanna think about the sun
No, not tonight.
Oh, it's wonderful, you being here with me
Close your eyes so you can see.

5/02 (442)